D0547828

SPELLING YEAR 6

Ages 10–11

SCHOLASTIC

Published in the UK by Scholastic Education, 2020
Book End, Range Road, Witney,
Oxfordshire, OX29 0YD
A division of Scholastic Limited

London – New York – Toronto – Sydney – Auckland
Mexico City – New Delhi – Hong Kong

www.scholastic.co.uk

1 2 3 4 5 6 7 8 9   0 1 2 3 4 5 6 7 8 9

British Library Cataloguing-in-Publication Data
A catalogue record for this book is available from the British Library.

ISBN 978-1407-18345-9

Printed and bound by Ashford Colour Press

Papers used by Scholastic Limited are made from wood grown in sustainable forests.

Author
Shelley Welsh

Editorial
Rachel Morgan, Vicki Yates, Suzanne Adams, Julia Roberts

Design
Dipa Mistry and QBS Learning

Cover Illustration
Clau Souza @Bright Agency

Contents

How to use this book

This book contains eleven different spelling practices based on key spelling topics to be covered in Year 6. There are also seven mixed spelling tests.

Spelling practice

Throughout each spelling practice there are short explanations recapping the rules or the focus and providing further guidance where necessary. There are up to five questions in each spelling practice, which challenge the children to complete parts of words or sentences, sort spellings into categories, complete crosswords or word searches, and so on.

At the end of each practice section, you will find a weekly spelling list and a section for children to note down any spellings they struggled with. Ask your child to practise the weekly spelling lists using Look-Cover-Write-Check, employing the skills they have learned. Encourage them to write down words they need more practice with in the 'words I struggled with' space and encourage them to practise these words too. It is intended that children will take around ten minutes to complete each spelling practice.

Spelling tests

There are ten questions in each spelling test which amount to ten marks. Read each spelling number followed by *The word is...* Leave at least a 12-second gap between spellings. More information can be found on page 57.

Prefixes
Spelling practice 1

10 MINS

A prefix is a string of letters that can be added to the beginning of a word to change its meaning. Adding a prefix does not change the spelling of the word.

1. Select a prefix from the box to give the words listed below an **opposite** meaning. Write each new word on the line provided.

| in | mis | dis | un | il | im | ir |

understand _____

fasten _____

legal _____

respect _____

regular _____

practical _____

active _____

KEEP IT GOING!

2. Solve the clues to help you complete each word below with the correct **prefix**.

An action that occurs between two or more people or things.

| | | | | | a | c | t | i | o | n |

A person who has become a celebrity.

| | | | | | s | t | a | r |

To build again.

| | | c | o | n | s | t | r | u | c | t |

The part of your mind that remembers information even when you aren't trying to.

| | | | | c | o | n | s | c | i | o | u | s |

To pause or break.

| | | | | c | o | n | t | i | n | u | e |

3. Choose a **prefix** from below to write on the line in front of each word.

super   auto   anti

_____social   _____biography   _____impose

_____graph   _____clockwise   _____natural

_____human   _____septic   _____pilot

CHECK IN A DICTIONARY

10 MINS

Weekly spelling list:

reapply	autobiography	submerge	superhuman
disapprove	disobey	imperfect	misspell
inactive	irrelevant	illogical	impatient
deactivate	dehydrate	untie	interact

Words I struggled with:

Well done! END OF SPELLING PRACTICE 1!

Suffixes 1

Spelling practice 2

A suffix is a letter or string of letters that can be added to the end of a root word to make a new word.

Sometimes, the spelling of the root word changes when the suffix is added.

The suffix **en** can be simply added to most words ending in two consonants or a long vowel sound and a consonant:

soft ⟶ soften; cheap ⟶ cheapen.

If a word ends in **e**, just add **n**:

wide ⟶ widen.

If a word ends in a short vowel sound and a consonant, the consonant is doubled before adding **en**:

sad ⟶ sadden.

1. Circle the **three** incorrect spellings below. Then write them correctly on the lines underneath.

deeppen   ripen   loossen   frighten   biten   hidden

_____   _____   _____

The suffix **ation** can be added to words ending in a consonant without changing the spelling: **vex** ⟶ **vexation**. If the word ends in **e**, the **e** is dropped: **observe** ⟶ **observation**.

The suffix **ly** is added to most root words without changing the spelling: **most** ⟶ **mostly**. If the root word ends in **y** with a consonant before it, the **y** is changed to **i**, but only if the root word has more than one syllable: **angry** ⟶ **angrily**.

If the root word ends with **ic**, **ally** is added instead of **ly**: **music** ⟶ **musically** (although there are exceptions).

2. Add either **ation** or **ly** to the words in brackets and write them on the lines provided.

Gwen _____ (usual) has some interesting

_____ (inform) when she comes in on Monday mornings.

She lives on a farm and _____ (basic) she spends the

whole weekend working. Gwen is _____ (complete)

happy to do so as she _____ (real) loves animals.

This week, she showed us photos of some newborn lambs and

we all looked in _____ (adore) at them

_____ (happy) snuggling up to their mothers.

KEEP IT GOING!

Suffixes 1
Spelling practice 2

The suffixes **ify**, **ate** and **ise** can be added to some root words without changes to the spelling: **fossil** ⟶ **fossilise**; **design** ⟶ **designate**.

For other words, you will need to make spelling adjustments:
priority ⟶ **prioritise**.

If the root word ends in **e**, remove the **e**: **intense** ⟶ **intensify**.

3. Create new words by choosing the correct **suffix** for each word below. One has been done for you.

| sign | strength | donation | communication |

| thick | cremation | liquid | flat |

| recognition | horror | solid | special |

ate	ify
communicate	

ise	en

11

10 MINS

Weekly spelling list:

LOOK
COVER
WRITE
CHECK ✓

usual	usually	inform	information
basic	basically	complete	completely
adore	adoration	hidden	loosen
intense	intensify	satisfaction	satisfy

Words I struggled with:

Well done! END OF SPELLING PRACTICE 2!

Suffixes 2

Spelling practice 3

10 MINS

When adding a suffix beginning with a vowel to a word ending in **fer**, the **r** is doubled if the syllable **fer** is still stressed after adding the suffix. If the syllable **fer** is not stressed, the **r** is not doubled. Say the words below each heading out loud to check the stressed syllable and notice the spelling:

root	+	ed	+	ing	+	al	+	ence
refer		referred		referring		referral		reference

1. Choose a different suffix for each word below. Then say your new word aloud to check whether the syllable **fer** is stressed. Use the spelling rules above to help you check your spelling.

   ed   **al**   **ing**   **ence**

   transfer_____   offer_____

   infer_____   prefer_____

The suffixes **tial** and **cial** both sound the same (/shul/). After a consonant, **tial** is mainly used; after a vowel, **cial** is usually used.

2. Add **tial** or **cial** to the words below. Remember to change the spelling of the root word if necessary.

   office   _____   sacrifice   _____

   resident _____   president   _____

13

3. Remember, there are exceptions to the rules for adding **tial** or **cial**, as you will find with some of the following. Write the new words below.

confidence _____

palace _____

commerce _____

benefit _____

The suffixes **tious** and **cious** sound the same (/shus/). If the root word ends in **ce**, **cious** is used; if the root word ends in **tion**, **tious** is used. Sometimes there won't be an obvious root to help you!

4. Mark these spellings right or wrong. Use a dictionary to check, then rewrite the incorrect words correctly below.

CHECK IN A DICTIONARY Aa

✗ or ✓

infectious ☐   gratious ☐

delicious ☐   ferotious ☐

conscientious ☐   pretencious ☐

_____

_____

10 MINS

LOOK COVER WRITE CHECK ✓

Weekly spelling list:

infer	inferred	prefer	preference
refer	referring	reference	referee
facial	financial	ambitious	nutritious
torrential	potential	repetitious	suspicious

Words I struggled with:

Well done! END OF SPELLING PRACTICE 3!

Suffixes 3
Spelling practice 4

10 MINS

Words ending in the /shun/ sound can have the spelling **tion**, **sion**, **ssion** or **cian**.

If the root word ends in **t** or **te**, use **tion**.

1. Add **tion** to the root words below, writing the new word on the line next to each. After you have checked your spelling using a dictionary, do Look-Cover-Write-Check using the additional lines.

act _____ _____

inject _____ _____

complete _____ _____

hesitate _____ _____

> You may need to alter the spelling of the root word before adding the suffix.

If the root word ends in **ss** or **mit**, use **ssion**.

2. Add the correct **suffix** to the root words below, writing the new word on the line next to each.

admit _____   permit _____

possess _____   express _____

omit _____   discuss _____

16

If the root word ends in **d** or **se**, use **sion**. Watch out for exceptions to this rule!

3. Solve the clues to help you complete each word below.

Growth or enlargement.

e	x							

Stress or anxiety.

t	e	n				

"Pay _____!" instructed the teacher.

a	t	t					

If the root word ends in **c** or **cs**, use **cian**. There are some exceptions.

4. These words end in **c** or **cs** but they don't all take the suffix **cian** to form a new word. Write the four that do take the **cian** suffix below.

basic   music   politics   epic   mathematics   electric

_____   _____

_____   _____

10 MINS

Weekly spelling list:

action	politician	electrician	hesitation
admission	injection	completion	expression
omission	discussion	possession	permission
expansion	comprehension	tension	procession

Words I struggled with:

Well done! END OF SPELLING PRACTICE 4!

Suffixes 4

Spelling practice 5

10 MINS

The suffixes **ant** and **ent** sound very similar because the sound they make is not emphasised. The same is true for **ance** and **ence**, **ancy** and **ency**.

Words ending in **ation** often use the endings **ant**, **ance** and **ancy**: **hesitation, hesitant, hesitance, hesitancy**.

After a soft /c/ or /g/ sound or **qu**, use the endings **ent**, **ence** and **ency**: **decent** ⟶ **decency**; **frequent** ⟶ **frequency**. Also use these endings in a word with a clear 'ch' sound in the right place: **confidence, silent**.

Remember, not all words follow these rules!

I. Complete the sentences using the words in brackets with their appropriate endings.

Anika was rather _____ (hesitate) when she approached the climbing wall.

Following the _____ (emerge) of new evidence, the police were able to arrest the suspect.

Izzy's dad has been a teaching _____ (assist) for ten years.

Our new puppy is very _____ (disobey) despite weeks of training.

KEEP IT GOING!

19

2. Circle the **correct spelling** to complete each sentence below.

a. Mr Jain attended a conference / conferance with other teachers.

b. The monarch's London residance / residence is Buckingham Palace.

c. My uncle speaks French and German with great fluency / fluancy.

d. The head teacher is dealing with truancy / truency among some of the older pupils.

---

3. Add the appropriate **suffix** to the root words below, writing the new word on the line next to each. After you have checked your spelling in a dictionary, use Look-Cover-Write-Check using the additional lines.

Root word	ant or ent ending	
contest		
reside		
dominate		
buoy		
oppose		
correspond		

10 MINS

4. Find the **nine** incorrectly spelled words and write them correctly on the lines below.

agent   pregnant   efficiant   emergant   agency

ascendant   emergence   transparent   agancy

evidant   pregnent   efficient   ascendent   efficiency

evidence   transparency   emergent   transparant

emergance   pregnancy   emergency   efficiancy

_____ _____ _____

_____ _____ _____

_____ _____ _____

5. Unravel these anagrams to spell words ending with **ent**, **ant**, **ence** and **ance**.

depend**ent**in   _____

anceradi   _____

form**ant**in   _____

ist**ence**ex   _____

10 MINS

Weekly spelling list:

vacant	vacancy	descent	descendant
hesitant	hesitance	assistant	assistance
truant	truancy	buoyant	buoyancy
frequent	frequency	fluent	fluency

Words I struggled with:

Well done! END OF SPELLING PRACTICE 5!

Suffixes 5

Spelling practice 6

10 MINS

The suffixes **able** and **ible** sound very similar because the sound they make is not stressed. The same is true for **ably** and **ibly**.

The ending **able** can often be added to a word without needing to change the spelling. If you add **able** or **ably** to words ending in **e**, drop the **e** before adding the suffix.

If you add **able** or **ably** to a word ending in **ce** or **ge**, keep the **e** when adding the suffix.

If you remove **able** from a word, you are often left with a complete word.

I. Add **able** to the following words. After you have checked your spelling using a dictionary, do Look-Cover-Write-Check using the additional lines.

depend _____ _____

notice _____ _____

change _____ _____

adore _____ _____

Suffixes 5

Spelling practice 6

10 MINS

There are fewer words ending in **ible** and **ibly**. For words ending in **e**, drop the **e** before adding these suffixes. If you remove **ible** or **ibly** from a word, you are not usually left with an obvious root word.

2. Make any necessary spelling adjustments before adding **ible** to each word. Write the correct word on the line.

flex   +   ible = _____

response +   ible = _____

force   +   ible = _____

digest   +   ible = _____

3. Six words in the passage below have been written with the incorrect suffix. Write these words correctly on the lines below.

> The weather has changed quite noticably over the last few decades. We used to have reasonily agreeable summers and much harsher winters. Nowadays, summer tends to start early and can be uncomfortibly hot by June or July, while winter months are considerably unpredictible. Some world leaders behave quite irresponsably when asked to address global warming issues so we should all take responsibility – our planet is irreplacable!

_____   _____   _____

_____   _____   _____

24

10 MINS

1. Complete the crossword using the clues below.

Crossword grid:

Across row 1: ¹h o r r ²i _ _ _
²i column: n, d
³r e l i _ _ (with ⁴l)
⁴l column: i, k, e
⁵i column: i, r, r, e, v, e, r, s
⁷c o m f o r t _ _
⁶s column: s, e, n, s
⁸a u d _ _ _ _

Across

1. "This holiday is going _____ wrong!" groaned Dad. (8)

3. Someone or something you can depend on. (8)

7. My bed is soft and _____. (10)

8. A sound that you can hear. (7)

Down

2. Something too awful to eat. (8)

4. Someone or something pleasant. (8)

5. When you can't change something. (12)

6. The behaviour expected of a Year 6 pupil. (8)

25

10 MINS

5. Complete the table using the words below so that they end in **ible**. They are tricky because they don't follow the rule!

CHECK IN A DICTIONARY

	ible
divide	
admit	
vision	

10 MINS

LOOK COVER WRITE CHECK ✔

Weekly spelling list:

invincible	deplorable	horribly	fashionable
convertible	unavoidably	sustainable	notably
terribly	intelligible	serviceable	bearable
respectable	irresponsible	considerably	noticeably

Words I struggled with:

Well done! END OF SPELLING PRACTICE 6!

Spelling ei or ie words

Spelling practice 7

10 MINS

For most words with an /ee/ sound, the spelling is **ie**. You may have heard the spelling rule '**i** before **e** except after **c**, but only when it rhymes with **bee**'. In other words, the /ee/ sound after the soft letter **c** is usually spelled **ei**.

1. Write as many words as you can think of that have the /ee/ sound spelled **ie** or **ei**.

CHECK IN A DICTIONARY **Aa**

_____ _____ _____

_____ _____ _____

_____ _____ _____

2. Use the clues and the spelling rules to complete the words.

A female family relative.

n			c	e

To grab hold of.

s			z	e

To be dishonest with someone.

d	e	c			v	e

To be aware of something.

p	e	r	c			v	e

Some words with an /ay/ sound use the spelling **ei**: **sleigh**.

3. Unscramble the anagrams to find words with the /ay/ sound spelled **ei**.

bourn**ei**gh _____   wght**ei** _____

gnr**ei** _____   n**ei**v _____

4. Use the column headings to sort these words into the table.

receive   neither   yield   shriek   piece   either

perceive   receipt   grief   fierce   seize   ceiling

disbelief   caffeine   siege   weird   protein   deceit

Words with an /ee/ sound and ie spelling	Words with an /ee/ sound spelled ei after a soft c	Exceptions to the rule

Say the words below out loud. Do you think they belong in any of the columns above? Why/why not?

height   conceited   icier   counterfeit   species   glacier

_____

_____

_____

_____

10 MINS

Weekly spelling list:

LOOK
COVER
WRITE
CHECK ✔

receipt	glacier	deceit	seize
conceit	receive	ceiling	niece
caffeine	conceive	neither	weird
eighteen	protein	deceive	sleigh

Words I struggled with:

_____

_____

_____

_____

_____

_____

> Well done! END OF SPELLING PRACTICE 7!

31

Words of foreign origin

Spelling practice 8

10 MINS

Many words in our English vocabulary originate from other languages, such as French and Italian. Some words which have a /k/ sound are spelled **ch** and are Greek in origin.

I. Highlight the **eleven** words in this word search with the /k/ sound spelled **ch**. Then write each word on the lines below.

v	x	q	r	d	x	h	p	c	w	z	z	q
b	t	s	c	h	e	m	e	h	l	c	j	v
z	v	m	h	q	m	e	q	a	c	h	e	n
e	c	h	o	v	q	c	v	r	q	e	x	m
q	h	q	r	n	v	h	n	a	v	m	y	s
v	a	r	u	m	n	a	m	c	n	i	q	c
n	o	y	s	j	m	n	b	t	m	s	v	h
m	s	a	r	c	h	i	t	e	c	t	n	o
j	k	p	w	z	x	c	m	r	n	j	m	o
c	h	r	o	n	o	l	o	g	i	c	a	l

1. _____   5. _____   9. _____

2. _____   6. _____   10. _____

3. _____   7. _____   11. _____

4. _____   8. _____

32

Some words which have a /sh/ sound are spelled **ch** and are French in origin. For example, **chef**.

2. The following words are French in origin but the /sh/ sound has been spelled incorrectly. Write the correct spelling next to each.

mashine _____

shalet _____

broshure _____

parashute _____

sharade _____

shateau _____

Some words which end with a /g/ sound are spelled **gue**, and others which end with a /k/ sound are spelled **que**. These are also French in origin.

3. Insert the **missing letters** to complete the words ending in a /g/ sound or a /k/ sound.

ton __ __ __   uni __ __ __

lea __ __ __   anti __ __ __

va __ __ __   grotes __ __ __

Many prefixes, suffixes and whole words come from Latin and Greek.

4. Use the Greek words on the left to complete the words on the right. You may have to make some changes to the spelling. One has been done for you.

Greek

agro   _agri_culture

autos   _____pilot

tele   _____scope

bios   _____graphy

phobo   claustro_____

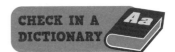

CHECK IN A DICTIONARY

Weekly spelling list:

scheme	tongue	mosque	technique
echo	chorus	chef	cheque
chaos	chronological	moustache	architect
machine	chateau	charade	chalet

Words I struggled with:

_____

_____

_____

_____

_____

_____

Well done! END OF SPELLING PRACTICE 8!

Silent letters

Spelling practice 9

10 MINS

To help you spell words with silent letters, try pronouncing the silent letter when you say the word out loud. There are patterns that can be observed in some words containing silent letters. For example, **island**, **aisle**, **isle**. (The silent letter **s** comes before the letter **l** and after the letter **i**.)

I. Circle the **silent letter** in the words below then write about the pattern you observe. The first has been done for you.

ⓚnock   ⓚnit   ⓚnead   ⓚnob

<u>Silent 'k' comes at the beginning of a word, before the letter 'n'.</u>

gnome   gnash   gnarled   foreign

_____

_____

comb   tomb   debt   subtle

_____

_____

isosceles   scientific   scissors   fluorescent

_____

_____

2. There are two words in each sentence below with missing **silent letters**. Circle the words then write them correctly in the spaces next to each sentence.

Sentence	Word 1	Word 2
In sience today, we learned about the musles in our body and how they move.		
The vicious creature nashed its teeth but the gards held the chains firmly.		
I'd love samon for dinner but I dout Mum has had a chance to go to the shops.		
By choosing to buy an electric veicle, our family is doing its bit for the enviroment.		

KEEP IT GOING!

Weekly spelling list:

thistle	rhombus	sandwich	doubt
lamb	listen	write	thumb
isosceles	solemn	autumn	wrong
cupboard	rhythm	ascend	knowledge

Words I struggled with:

_____

_____

_____

_____

_____

Well done! END OF SPELLING PRACTICE 9!

Homophones
Spelling practice 10

10 MINS

Words with the same, or very similar, sounds but different spellings are called **homophones**.

Some words are not true homophones but are near homophones and these can be easily confused.

1. Choose the correct **homophone** from below for each of the following definitions.

draught   draft   allowed

aloud   stationery   stationary

Definition	Word
first attempt at a piece of writing	_____
audible	_____
a current of cool air	_____
not moving	_____
permitted	_____
paper, envelopes	_____

KEEP IT GOING!

2. Use the clues to complete the crossword. The homophones are in a box below to help you.

principle / principal	naval / navel
oar / or	road / rode
	lead / led

Across

1. A coordinating conjunction. (2)

4. Past tense of 'ride'. (4)

5. A button in your tummy. (5)

6. Another word for head teacher. (9)

9. To do with sailors. (5)

10. Past tense of 'lead'. (3)

Down

2. Something you drive on. (4)

3. A basic rule. (9)

7. A heavy metal or a verb. (4)

8. You row with this. (3)

10 MINS

3. Write a matching **homophone** or **near homophone** for each of the following words.

alter   _____

pour   _____

groan   _____

paws   _____

seen   _____

past   _____

rays   _____

waist   _____

complement   _____

practice   _____

loose   _____

precede   _____

flex   _____

devise   _____

10 MINS

LOOK COVER WRITE CHECK ✔

Weekly spelling list:

steal	steel	profit	prophet
grown	groan	guest	guessed
root	route	affect	effect
bridal	bridle	heard	herd

Words I struggled with:

Well done! END OF SPELLING PRACTICE 10!

Tricky words

Spelling practice 11

10 MINS

One way of learning to spell tricky words is to divide them into syllables, especially words where a vowel appears in an unstressed syllable: sep**a**rate.

For words with silent letters, it is useful to pronounce the silent letter to help with spelling.

However, most tricky words just have to be learned! Try to think of your own strategies, such as for how to spell **because**: '**b**ig **e**lephants **c**an **a**lways **u**nderstand **s**mall **e**lephants'.

1. In each of the words below, there is a **missing vowel** where a syllable is unstressed. Rewrite the words correctly, then use your dictionary to check your spelling. Write any corrections on the additional lines provided.

privlege _____ _____

defnite _____ _____

desprate _____ _____

temprature _____ _____

marvllous _____ _____

categry _____ _____

CHECK IN A DICTIONARY

2. Find the **twelve** words in the paragraph that have been spelled incorrectly and write them correctly on the lines below.

Last Wenesday was Dad's birthday and my famly and I went for a celebratry meal to a local restaurant. My sister was keen to try the nachos and although I was doutful, she persaded me to taste one. Personly, I think she exagerated how nice they would be! "I garantee that my spicy vegtable curry is better," I told her. She took an experimentle spoonful then she had to agree how marvellous it was. She said she would definitly choose the curry next time as she had thoroghly enjoyed tasting mine.

_____   _____   _____

_____   _____   _____

_____   _____   _____

_____   _____   _____

KEEP IT GOING!

44

3. Divide the following tricky words into **separate syllables** and say them out loud. Then use Look-Cover-Write-Check, writing any corrections on the additional lines.

conscience _____ _____

apostrophe _____ _____

separate _____ _____

embarrass _____ _____

Weekly spelling list:

developed	occurrence	necessarily	interrupt
disastrous	courageous	definitely	curiosity
conscious	controversy	awkward	biscuit
thorough	mischievous	secretary	excited

Words I struggled with:

Well done! END OF SPELLING PRACTICE 11!

Spelling Test 1

Marks

1. The celebration started to go _____ wrong.

2. Mum met the _____ of Ireland on holiday.

3. I asked Hamish to move but he wouldn't _____.

4. The greengrocer _____ the potatoes.

5. The security officer made a _____ _____ search of my case.

6. Faisul uses a _____ to style his hair.

7. Millie _____ the ball to her little brother.

8. The _____ _____ made its way down the street.

9. We investigated the properties of a square-based

   _____ in maths.

10. The _____ of the next-door flat is very noisy.

◯

10

Well done! END OF SPELLING TEST 1!

47

Marks

1. Amira is staying in a _____ over the holidays.

2. Joe had a _____ idea of where he'd left his homework.

3. We took the _____ route to the seaside.

4. The policeman gave us a _____ reminder to be vigilant.

5. Dad took me to the _____ for some throat tablets.

6. Meghan began to _____ her model.

7. I would have _____ fish but I was given chicken.

8. My aunt is finding her _____ quite tiring.

9. Mani was _____ in capturing the escaped snake.

10. The islands had a range of _____ wildlife species.

10

Well done! END OF SPELLING TEST 2!

Spelling Test 3

Marks

1. Finn _____ the last answer in the test.

2. There was a _____ between two vehicles outside school.

3. It was agreed that the sports celebrity's behaviour was

   _____.

4. We wrote about the _____ of the water cycle.

5. Brogan's bike is in poor _____.

6. Samara _____ her mum and carried on talking.

7. Following the _____, the politician lost his job.

8. The weather forecast isn't _____ accurate.

9. Please can you reply to me at your _____.

10. My brother _____ spilled some milk on the tablecloth.

10

Well done! END OF SPELLING TEST 3!

Marks

1. Henry's new puppy is _____.

2. Lise tends to _____ with her brother.

3. We lined up when we _____ the fire alarm sound.

4. My sister and I bought Mum a _____ treatment for Christmas.

5. Our teacher is usually _____ over lunchtime.

6. Cody's disappointment was _____.

7. Muslims worship in a _____.

8. It is possible to buy coffee without _____.

9. The end of term always brings a lot of _____.

10. The _____ fixed our wiring system.

10

Well done! END OF SPELLING TEST 4!

Spelling Test 5

Marks

1. Will kicked the ball _____ the hedge.

2. I _____ that we went out for tea.

3. My new walking boots are made of _____ leather.

4. Max held out his hands to _____ his prize.

5. We shouted in the cave so we could hear the

   _____.

6. The Lord Mayor is a very _____ man.

7. When doing tests, every minute is _____!

8. My baby brother is _____ by the stars.

9. After the summer break, the politicians are now returning

   to _____.

10. Mum studied _____ before she became a business owner.

10

Well done! END OF SPELLING TEST 5!

10 MINS

Marks

1. The football team was _____ shocked to be beaten in the final.

2. I prefer _____ books to novels.

3. The _____ of a letter can be indicated by an apostrophe.

4. My music teacher said my singing was _____.

5. Chandra is playing the main _____ in the class play.

6. Luckily, Abi's awful ringtone is barely _____.

7. The jockey held the _____ tightly as the horse bolted.

8. Our doctor has sent a _____ for me to see an eye specialist.

9. Jed climbed the tree then sat on a _____ to look at the view.

10. Dad said it was _____ we apply for my passport this week.

10

Well done! END OF SPELLING TEST 6!

10 MINS

Marks

1. The newborn lamb was surprisingly _____ for one so young.

2. "Would you _____ Scotland for a holiday?" Billy asked Sam.

3. We called the hotel but there wasn't a _____.

4. Ciara is on the Pupil Voice _____.

5. My _____ of some words is different to yours.

6. Our teacher asked us _____ coat was left on the peg.

7. A team of huskies pulled the _____ across the frozen tundra.

8. I didn't intend to have more dessert but Mum can be quite

   _____.

9. It is _____ that you bring a water bottle on the trip.

10. Our neighbours have _____ grass, which saves them mowing.

10

Well done! END OF SPELLING TEST 7!

Answers

Spelling

Q	Answers for Prefixes
1	**mis**understand, **un**fasten, **il**legal, **dis**respect, **ir**regular, **im**practical, **in**active
2	**inter**action/**trans**action, **super**star, **re**construct, **sub**conscious, **dis**continue
3	**anti**social **auto**biography **super**impose **auto**graph **anti**clockwise **super**natural **super**human **anti**septic **auto**pilot

Q	Answers for Suffixes 1
1	deepen, loosen, bitten
2	usual**ly**, inform**ation**, basical**ly**, complete**ly**, real**ly**, ador**ation**, happi**ly**

3		ate	ify
		communicate	signify
		donate	horrify
		cremate	solidify
		ise	**en**
		liquidise	strengthen
		recognise	thicken
		specialise	flatten

Q	Answers for Suffixes 2
1	Any of the following: transfer**red**, transfer**ral**, transfer**ence**; offer**ed**, offer**ing**; infer**red**, infer**ring**, infer**ence**; prefer**red**, prefer**ring**, prefer**ence**
2	offi**cial**, residen**tial**, sacrifi**cial**, presiden**tial**
3	confiden**tial**, pala**tial**, commer**cial**, benefi**cial**
4	infectious ✓ gratious ✗ gracious ✓ delicious ✓ ferotious ✗ ferocious ✓ conscientious ✓ pretencious ✗ pretentious ✓

Q	Answers for Suffixes 3
1	ac**tion**, injec**tion**, comple**tion**, hesita**tion**
2	admi**ssion**, permi**ssion**, posse**ssion**, expre**ssion**, omi**ssion**, discu**ssion**
3	expan**sion**/exten**sion**, ten**sion**, atten**tion**
4	musi**cian**, politi**cian**, mathemati**cian**, electri**cian**

Q	Answers for Suffixes 4
1	hesit**ant**, emerg**ence**, assist**ant**, disobedi**ent**
2	confer**ence**, resid**ence**, flu**ency**, tru**ancy**
3	contest**ant**, resid**ent**, domin**ant**, buoy**ant**, oppon**ent**, correspond**ent**
4	The following words are incorrectly spelled: efficiant, emergant, agancy, evidant, pregnent, ascendent, transparant, emergance, officiency. The correct spellings are: efficient, emergent, agency, evident, pregnant, ascendant, transparency, emergence, efficiency
5	independ**ent**, radi**ance**, inform**ant,** exist**ence**

Q	Answers for Suffixes 5
1	depend**able**, notice**able**, change**able**, ador**able**
2	flex**ible**, respons**ible**, forc**ible**, digest**ible**
3	noticeably, reasonably, uncomfortably, unpredictable, irresponsibly, irreplaceable
4	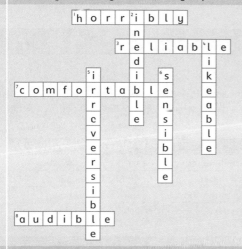

For question 4 crossword:
- horribly
- reliable
- comfortable
- audible
- indivisible (down)
- sensible (down)
- likeable (down)

5		**ible**
	divide	divisible
	admit	admissible
	vision	visible

Q	Answers for ei or ie spellings
1	Accept correctly spelled words with the /ee/ sound spelled **ie** or **ei**, for example: ceiling, receive, receipt, chief, piece
2	niece, seize, deceive, perceive
3	neighbour, weight, reign, vein

	Words with an /ee/ sound and **ie** spelling		Words with an /ee/ sound spelled **ei** after a soft **c**		Exceptions to the rule	
4	yield	fierce	receive	perceive	neither	protein
	shriek	piece	receipt	deceit	caffeine	weird
	siege	disbelief	ceiling		either	seize
	grief					

Additional task: answers will vary. For example, 'Height and counterfeit don't belong because they don't have an /ee/ sound.' 'Conceited belongs because it has an /ee/ sound spelled 'ei' after a soft 'c'.' 'Glacier, icier and species don't belong because they have an /ee/ sound after a soft 'c' which is spelled 'ie'.'

1

v	x	q	r	d	x	h	p	c	w	z	z	q
b	t	s	c	h	e	m	e	h	l	c	j	v
z	v	m	h	q	m	e	q	a	c	h	e	n
e	c	h	o	v	q	c	v	r	q	e	x	m
q	h	q	r	n	v	h	n	a	v	m	y	s
v	a	r	u	m	n	a	m	c	n	i	q	c
n	o	y	s	j	m	n	b	t	m	s	v	h
m	s	a	r	c	h	i	t	e	c	t	n	o
j	k	p	w	z	x	c	m	r	n	j	m	o
c	h	r	o	n	o	l	o	g	i	c	a	l

2 ma**ch**ine, **ch**alet, bro**ch**ure, para**ch**ute, **ch**arade, **ch**ateau

3 ton**gue**, uni**que**, lea**gue**, va**gue**, anti**que,** grotes**que**

4 **auto**pilot, **tele**scope, **bio**graphy, claustro**phobic**

1
Answers will vary. For example:
◯gnome, ◯gnash, ◯gnarled, forei◯gn - silent **g** comes before the letter **n**
com◯b, tom◯b, de◯bt, su◯btle - silent **b** at the end of a word comes after the letter **m** and in the middle of a word before the letter **t**
isosceles, scientific, scissors, fluorescent - silent **c** comes after the letter **s** (Note: the **sc** spelling of the /s/ sound is often found in words of Latin origin)

2

Sentence	Word 1	Word 2
In sience today, we learned about the musles in our body and how they move.	science	muscles
The vicious creature nashed its teeth but the gards held the chains firmly.	gnashed	guards
I'd love samon for dinner but I dout Mum has had a chance to go to the shops.	salmon	doubt
By choosing to buy an electric veicle, our family is doing its bit for the enviroment.	vehicle	environment

1
first attempt at a piece of writing – draft; audible – aloud; a current of cool air – draught;
not moving – stationary; permitted – allowed; paper, envelopes – stationery

2

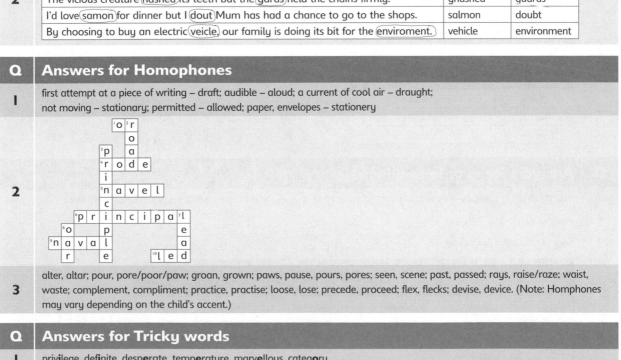

3 alter, altar; pour, pore/poor/paw; groan, grown; paws, pause, pours, pores; seen, scene; past, passed; rays, raise/raze; waist, waste; complement, compliment; practice, practise; loose, lose; precede, proceed; flex, flecks; devise, device. (Note: Homphones may vary depending on the child's accent.)

1 priv**i**lege, defin**i**te, des**pe**rate, temp**e**rature, marv**e**llous, categ**o**ry

2 Wednesday, family, celebratory, doubtful, persuaded, personally, exaggerated, guarantee, vegetable, experimental, definitely, thoroughly

3 Check that children have spelled each word correctly.

How to administer the spelling tests

There are seven short spelling tests in this book. Each test consists of ten questions. They should take around ten minutes to complete but you should allow your child as much time as they need to complete them.

Read the instructions in the box below. The instructions are similar to the ones given in the National Curriculum tests. This will familiarise children with the style and format of the tests and show them what to expect.

Listen carefully to the instructions I am going to give you.

I am going to read ten sentences to you. Each sentence on your answer sheet has a missing word. Listen carefully to the missing word and write it in the space provided, making sure you spell the word correctly. I will read the word, then the word within the sentence, then repeat the word a third time.

Do you have any questions?

Read the spellings as follows:

- Give the question number, 'Spelling 1'
- Say, 'The word is...'
- Read the whole sentence to show the word in context
- Repeat, 'The word is...'

Leave at least a 12-second gap between each spelling.

At the end re-read all ten questions. Then say, 'This is the end of the test. Please put down your pencil or pen.'

Each correct answer should be awarded **1 mark**.

Spelling test transcripts

Spelling Test 1

Spelling 1: The word is **horribly**.
The celebration started to go **horribly** wrong.
The word is **horribly**.

Spelling 2: The word is **president**.
Mum met the **president** of Ireland on holiday.
The word is **president**.

Spelling 3: The word is **budge**.
I asked Hamish to move but he wouldn't **budge**.
The word is **budge**.

Spelling 4: The word is **weighed**.
The greengrocer **weighed** the potatoes.
The word is **weighed**.

Spelling 5: The word is **thorough**.
The security officer made a **thorough** search of my case.
The word is **thorough**.

Spelling 6: The word is **comb**.
Faisal uses a **comb** to style his hair.
The word is **comb**.

Spelling 7: The word is **threw**.
Millie **threw** the ball to her little brother.
The word is **threw**.

Spelling 8: The word is **procession**.
The **procession** made its way down the street.
The word is **procession**.

Spelling 9: The word is **pyramid**.
We investigated the properties of a square-based **pyramid** in maths.
The word is **pyramid**.

Spelling 10: The word is **occupant**.
The **occupant** of the next-door flat is very noisy.
The word is **occupant**.

Spelling Test 2

Spelling 1: The word is **chalet**.
Amira is staying in a **chalet** over the holidays.
The word is **chalet**.

Spelling 2: The word is **vague**.
Joe had a **vague** idea of where he'd left his homework.
The word is **vague**.

Spelling 3: The word is **scenic**.
We took the **scenic** route to the seaside.
The word is **scenic**.

Spelling 4: The word is **cautious**.
The policeman gave us a **cautious** reminder to be vigilant.
The word is **cautious**.

Spelling 5: The word is **chemist**.
Dad took me to the **chemist** for some throat tablets.
The word is **chemist**.

Spelling 6: The word is **disassemble**.
Meghan began to **disassemble** her model.
The word is **disassemble**.

Spelling 7: The word is **preferred**.
I would have **preferred** fish but I was given chicken.
The word is **preferred**.

Spelling 8: The word is **pregnancy**.
My aunt is finding her **pregnancy** quite tiring.
The word is **pregnancy**.

Spelling 9: The word is **courageous**.
Mani was **courageous** in capturing the escaped snake.
The word is **courageous**.

Spelling 10: The word is **unique**.
The islands had a range of **unique** wildlife species.
The word is **unique**.

Spelling test transcripts

Spelling Test 3

Spelling 1: The word is **guessed**.
Finn **guessed** the last answer in the test.
The word is **guessed**.

Spelling 2: The word is **collision**.
There was a **collision** between two vehicles outside school.
The word is **collision**.

Spelling 3: The word is **unprofessional**.
It was agreed that the sports celebrity's behaviour was **unprofessional**.
The word is **unprofessional**.

Spelling 4: The word is **features**.
We wrote about the **features** of the water cycle.
The word is **features**.

Spelling 5: The word is **condition**.
Brogan's bike is in poor **condition**.
The word is **condition**.

Spelling 6: The word is **disobeyed**.
Samara **disobeyed** her mum and carried on talking.
The word is **disobeyed**.

Spelling 7: The word is **deception**.
Following the **deception**, the politician lost his job.
The word is **deception**.

Spelling 8: The word is **necessarily**.
The weather forecast isn't **necessarily** accurate.
The word is **necessarily**.

Spelling 9: The word is **convenience**.
Please can you reply to me at your **convenience**.
The word is **convenience**.

Spelling 10: The word is **accidentally**.
My brother **accidentally** spilled some milk on the tablecloth.
The word is **accidentally**.

Spelling Test 4

Spelling 1: The word is **adorable**.
Henry's new puppy is **adorable**.
The word is **adorable**.

Spelling 2: The word is **disagree**.
Lise tends to **disagree** with her brother.
The word is **disagree**.

Spelling 3: The word is **heard**.
We lined up when we **heard** the fire alarm sound.
The word is **heard**.

Spelling 4: The word is **facial**.
My sister and I bought Mum a **facial** treatment for Christmas.
The word is **facial**.

Spelling 5: The word is **available**.
Our teacher is usually **available** over lunchtime.
The word is **available**.

Spelling 6: The word is **immeasurable**.
Cody's disappointment was **immeasurable**.
The word is **immeasurable**.

Spelling 7: The word is **mosque**.
Muslims worship in a **mosque**.
The word is **mosque**.

Spelling 8: The word is **caffeine**.
It is possible to buy coffee without **caffeine**.
The word is **caffeine**.

Spelling 9: The word is **excitement**.
The end of term always brings a lot of **excitement**.
The word is **excitement**.

Spelling 10: The word is **electrician**.
The **electrician** fixed our wiring system.
The word is **electrician**.

Spelling test transcripts

Spelling Test 5

Spelling 1: The word is **through**.
Will kicked the ball **through** the hedge.
The word is **through**.

Spelling 2: The word is **suggested**.
I **suggested** that we went out for tea.
The word is **suggested**.

Spelling 3: The word is **tough**.
My new walking boots are made of **tough** leather.
The word is **tough**.

Spelling 4: The word is **receive**.
Max held out his hands to **receive** his prize.
The word is **receive**.

Spelling 5: The word is **echo**.
We shouted in the cave so we could hear the **echo**.
The word is **echo**.

Spelling 6: The word is **solemn**.
The Lord Mayor is a very **solemn** man.
The word is **solemn**.

Spelling 7: The word is **precious**.
When doing tests, every minute is **precious**!
The word is **precious**.

Spelling 8: The word is **fascinated**.
My baby brother is **fascinated** by the stars.
The word is **fascinated**.

Spelling 9: The word is **parliament**.
After the summer break, the politicians are now returning to **parliament**.
The word is **parliament**.

Spelling 10: The word is **accountancy**.
Mum studied **accountancy** before she became a business owner.
The word is **accountancy**.

Spelling Test 6

Spelling 1: The word is **totally**.
The football team was **totally** shocked to be beaten in the final.
The word is **totally**.

Spelling 2: The word is **reference**.
I prefer **reference** books to novels.
The word is **reference**.

Spelling 3: The word is **omission**.
The **omission** of a letter can be indicated by an apostrophe.
The word is **omission**.

Spelling 4: The word is **delightful**.
My music teacher said my singing was **delightful**.
The word is **delightful**.

Spelling 5: The word is **character**.
Chandra is playing the main **character** in the class play.
The word is **character**.

Spelling 6: The word is **audible**.
Luckily, Abi's awful ringtone is barely **audible**.
The word is **audible**.

Spelling 7: The word is **reins**.
The jockey held the **reins** tightly as the horse bolted.
The word is **reins**.

Spelling 8: The word is **referral**.
Our doctor has sent a **referral** for me to see an eye specialist.
The word is **referral**.

Spelling 9: The word is **bough**.
Jed climbed the tree then sat on a **bough** to look at the view.
The word is **bough**.

Spelling 10: The word is **crucial**.
Dad said it was **crucial** we apply for my passport this week.
The word is **crucial**.

Spelling test transcripts

Spelling Test 7

Spelling 1: The word is **nimble**.
The newborn lamb was surprisingly **nimble** for one so young.
The word is **nimble**.

Spelling 2: The word is **recommend**.
"Would you **recommend** Scotland for a holiday?" Billy asked Sam.
The word is **recommend**.

Spelling 3: The word is **vacancy**.
We called the hotel but there wasn't a **vacancy**.
The word is **vacancy**.

Spelling 4: The word is **committee**.
Ciara is on the Pupil Voice **committee**.
The word is **committee**.

Spelling 5: The word is **pronunciation**.
My **pronunciation** of some words is different to yours.
The word is **pronunciation**.

Spelling 6: The word is **whose**,
Our teacher asked us **whose** coat was left on the peg.
The word is **whose**.

Spelling 7: The word is **sleigh**.
A team of huskies pulled the **sleigh** across the frozen tundra.
The word is **sleigh**.

Spelling 8: The word is **persuasive**.
I didn't intend to have more dessert but Mum can be quite **persuasive**.
The word is **persuasive**.

Spelling 9: The word is **essential**.
It is **essential** that you bring a water bottle on the trip.
The word is **essential**.

Spelling 10: The word is **artificial**.
Our neighbours have **artificial** grass, which saves them mowing.
The word is **artificial**.

Progress chart

Fill in your score in the table below to see how well you've done.

Test number	Score	Percentage
Spelling Test 1	/10	
Spelling Test 2	/10	
Spelling Test 3	/10	
Spelling Test 4	/10	
Spelling Test 5	/10	
Spelling Test 6	/10	
Spelling Test 7	/10	

Percentage	
0–33%	Good try! You need more practice in some topics – ask an adult to help you.
34–69%	You're doing really well. Ask for extra help for any topics you found tricky.
70–100%	You're a 10-Minute SATs Test star – good work!

Reward Certificate

Well done!

You have completed all of the 10-Minute SATs Tests

Name: _____   Date: _____

SATs Made Simple

English

Maths

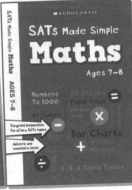

➡ **Covers all English and Maths SATs test topics**

➡ **Includes fun activities and skills check questions**

➡ **Ideal for extra practice at home**